Darth Vader ignites his lightsaber.

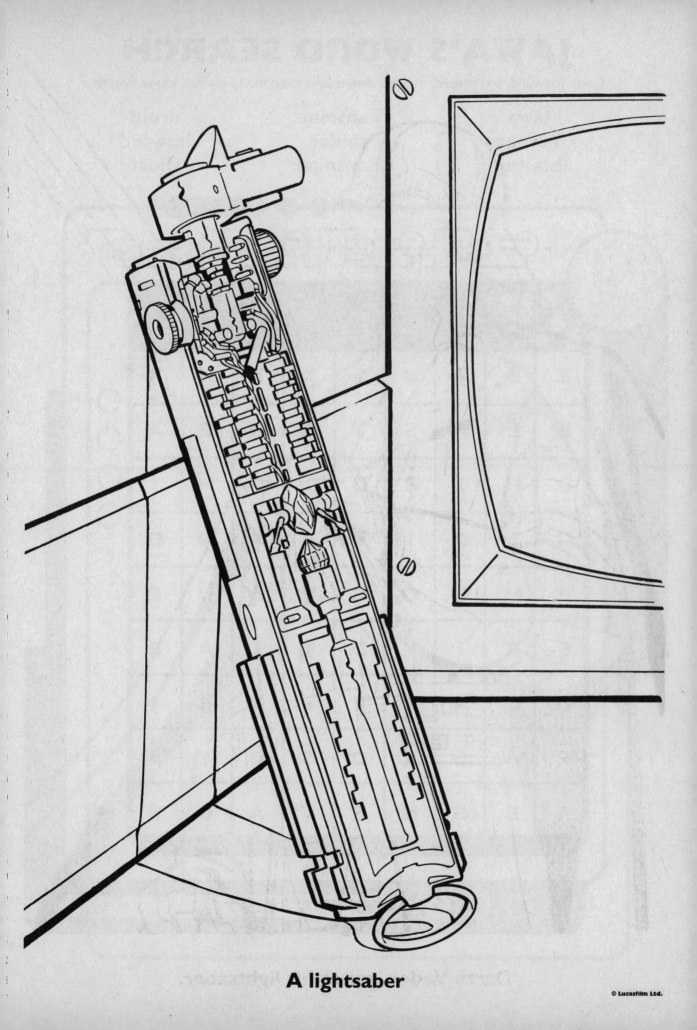

A lightsaber

JAWA'S WORD SEARCH

Look forward, backward, across, down and diagonally to find these words.

Jawa Tatooine droid
Tusken Raider hooded
blaster scavenger short

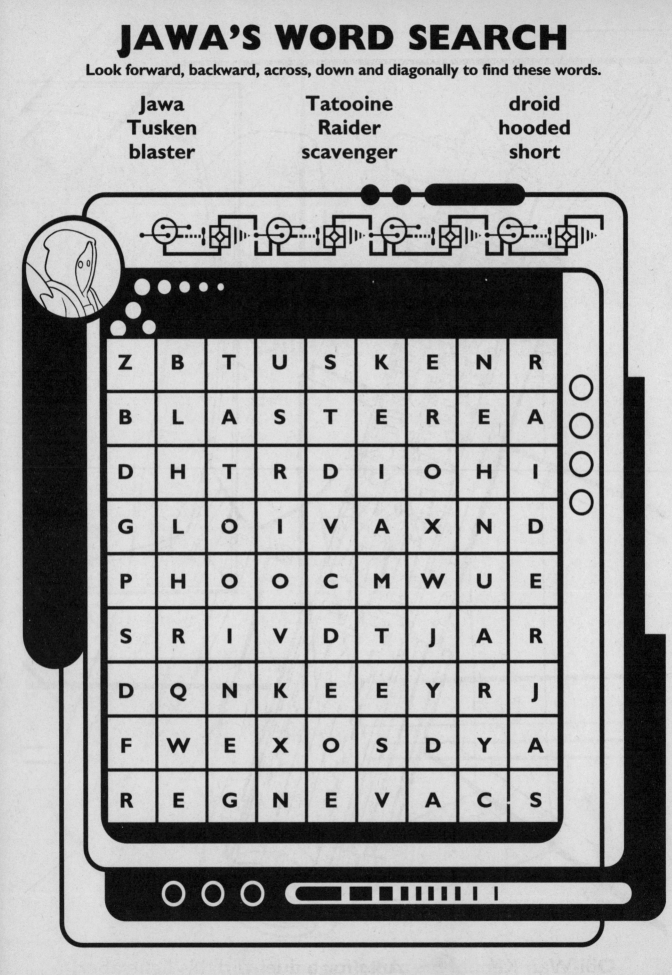

Z	B	T	U	S	K	E	N	R
B	L	A	S	T	E	R	E	A
D	H	T	R	D	I	O	H	I
G	L	O	I	V	A	X	N	D
P	H	O	O	C	M	W	U	E
S	R	I	V	D	T	J	A	R
D	Q	N	K	E	E	Y	R	J
F	W	E	X	O	S	D	Y	A
R	E	G	N	E	V	A	C	S

Obi-Wan Kenobi prepares for a duel with his lightsaber.

Emperor Palpatine is Darth Vader's master.

The Sith hate the Jedi.

Yoda is a Jedi Master.

He has trained many generations of Jedi.

**Luke has crashed his X-wing
on Dagobah, where Yoda lives.**

**Yoda lifts Luke's X-wing out of the mud
so Luke can help his friends.**

© Lucasfilm Ltd.

Yoda trains Luke to be a Jedi.

Training to be a Jedi is hard work.

JEDI TRAINING CROSSWORD PUZZLE

Down:

1. Yoda lives on the _____ system.
3. Yoda has long pointy _____ on the sides of his head.

Across:

2. Luke sees _____ in the cave.
4. _____ is a great Jedi Master.
5. On the Dagobah system there are many _____ and other creepy crawly life-forms.

WHICH YODA IS DIFFERENT?

A

B
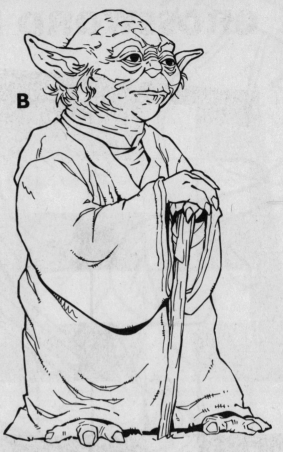

C

D

**Luke goes into a cave and
sees something that frightens him...**

It's Darth Vader!

HOW ARE DARTH VADER AND LUKE SKYWALKER RELATED?

A. FATHER AND SON

B. UNCLE AND NEPHEW

C. MOTHER AND DAUGHTER

D. SECOND COUSINS

DRAW THE OTHER HALF OF DARTH VADER'S HELMET.

**Darth Vader and Luke Skywalker
duel with their lightsabers.**

Luke duels valiantly.

CAN YOU ESCAPE
THE DEATH STAR MAZE...

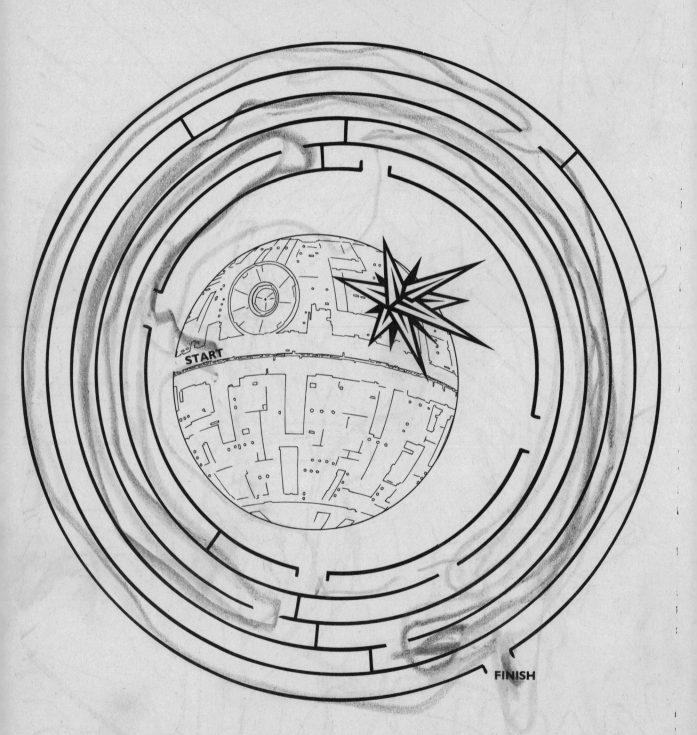

BEFORE IT EXPLODES?

Obi-Wan Kenobi

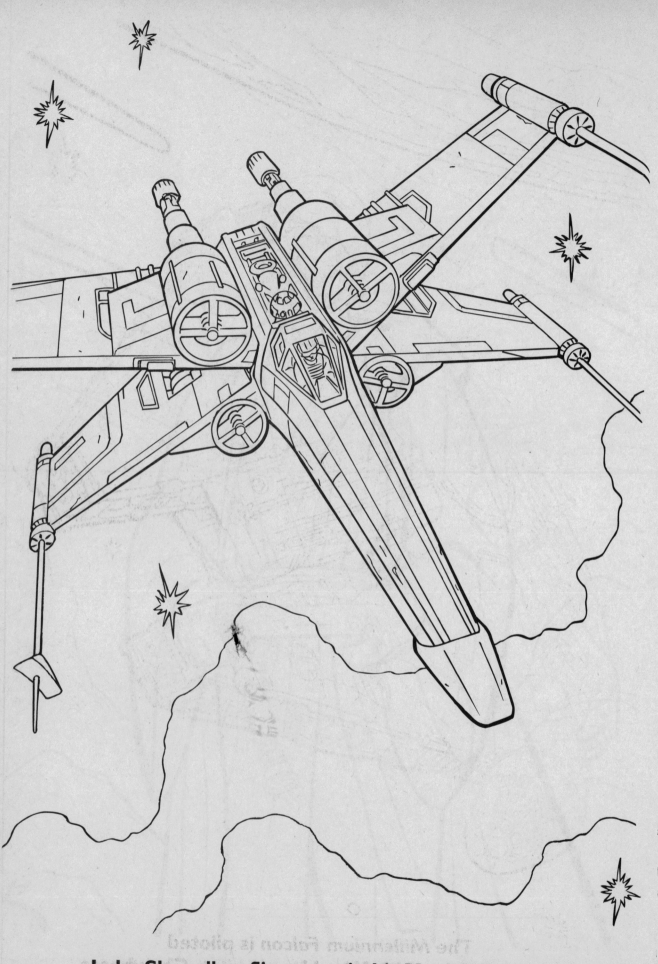

Luke Skywalker flies away in his X-wing fighter.

**The *Millennium Falcon* is piloted
by Han Solo and his Wookiee co-pilot, Chewbacca.**

Han and Chewbacca blast their way out of trouble.

WOOKIEE WORD SEARCH

Look forward, backward, across, down and diagonally to find these words.

Han Solo
Cloud City

Blaster
Carbonite
Chewie

Chewbacca
Falcon

C	A	R	B	O	N	I	T	E
L	H	A	N	S	O	L	O	F
O	C	E	I	W	E	H	C	A
U	R	Q	W	O	O	K	I	L
D	O	A	Z	B	Z	F	C	C
C	S	L	A	S	A	A	N	O
I	S	B	O	W	A	C	E	N
T	W	H	T	K	I	E	C	A
Y	R	E	T	S	A	L	B	A

"I see two banthas down there
but I don't see any Sand People."

BANTHA TRACKS

Can you lead the banthas through the desert maze?

START

FINISH

The Rebels have won a great battle.

They reward their heroes with medals.

An astromech droid

Droids make great friends.

R2-D2 and C-3PO have had many adventures.

There are many different kinds of astromech droids.
Color the two that are the same.

A

B

C

D

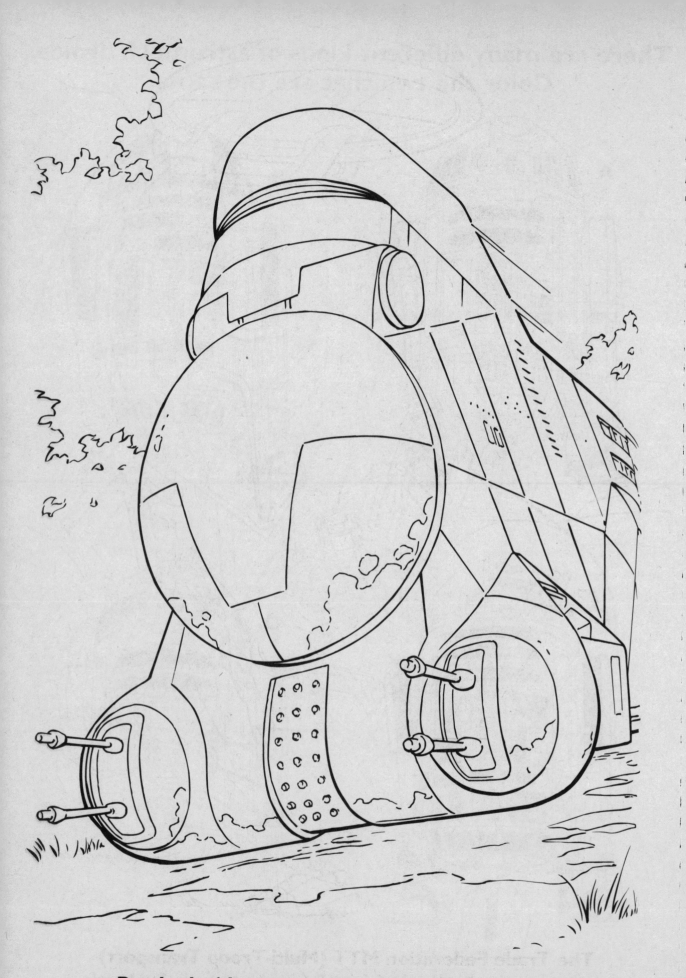

Battle droids use special vehicles for transport.

**The Trade Federation MTT (Multi-Troop Transport)
opens, and the battle droids unfold to get ready for battle.**

Which two droids are friends? Color them.

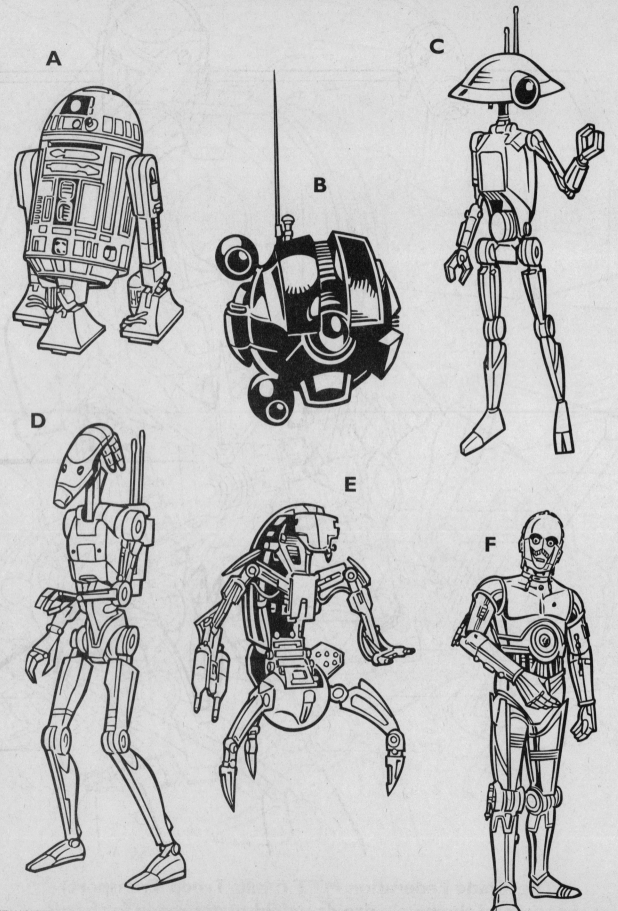

A

B

C

D

E

F

Some droids are dangerous.

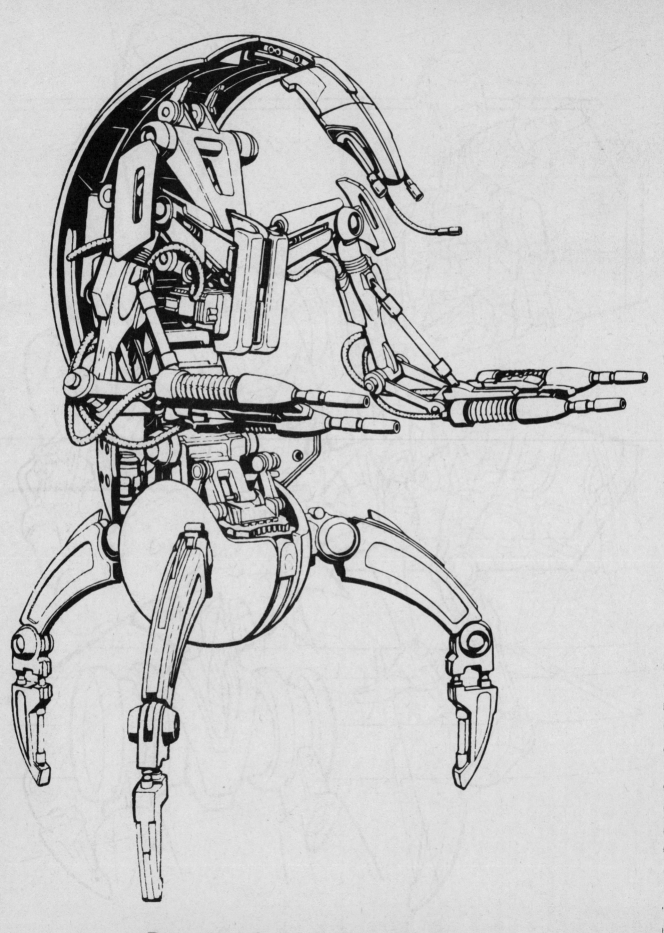

Destroyer droids have laser cannons.

Look out! They are firing!

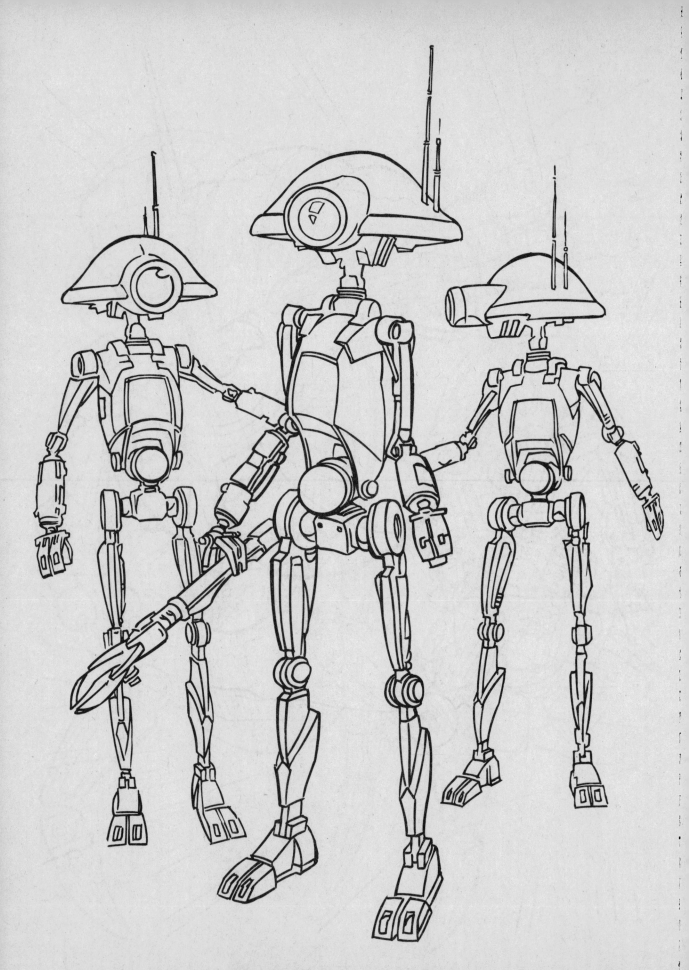

Some droids are small.

Some droids are no bigger than a ball.

Battle droids have captured Queen Amidala of Naboo.

Maybe R2-D2 and his friends can help.

Which three battle droids are different?

© Lucasfilm Ltd.

Connect the dots to see what kind of droid helps prepare for the Boonta Eve Podrace.

C-3PO meets R2-D2.

R2-D2 repairs a Podracer.

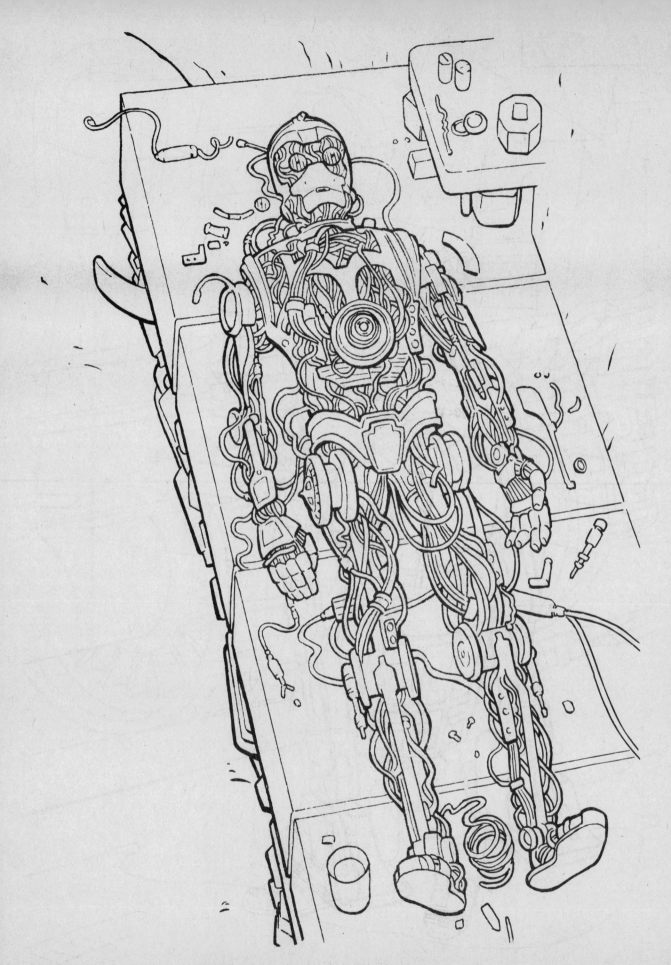

C-3PO is not quite finished yet.

TC-14 brings the waiting Jedi some refreshment.

Droid fighters can fly through space.
They look like space ships.

A Trade Federation battleship

Anakin and R2-D2 join the battle in a Naboo starfighter.

The queen has been captured!

Rune Haako

NUTE GUNRAY & RUNE HAAKO ARE MEMBERS OF WHAT ORGANIZATION?

A. THE TRADE FEDERATION

B. THE JEDI COUNCIL

C. THE IMPERIAL SENATE

D. THE HOLOCRON LIBRARY SOCIETY

DARTH MAUL'S
WORD SCRAMBLE

Unscramble the words below to see what is special about Darth Maul's lightsaber.

OWT LABESD

— — — — — — — — — — —

Nute Gunray

Darth Maul is a Sith apprentice...

...to his master Darth Sidious, a Sith Lord.

The Jedi will help protect Naboo...

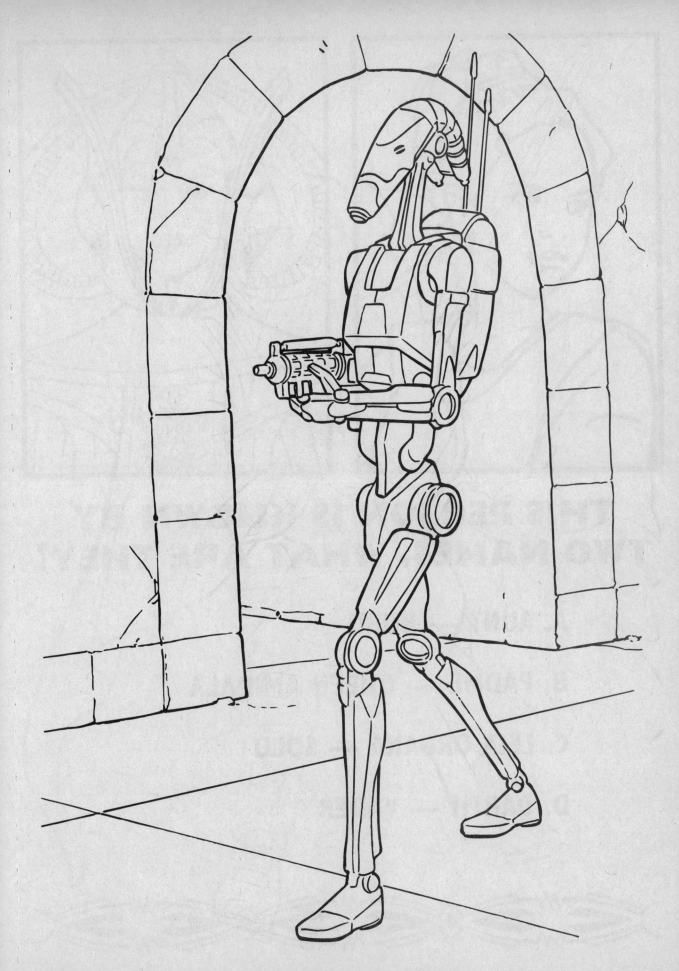

...from the battle droids.

THIS PERSON IS KNOWN BY TWO NAMES. WHAT ARE THEY?

A. AUNT — BURU

B. PADMÉ — QUEEN AMIDALA

C. LEIA ORGANA — SOLO

D. DARTH — VADER

BUILD-A-BOT

This battle droid is not finished. Draw a line to the part that completes him.

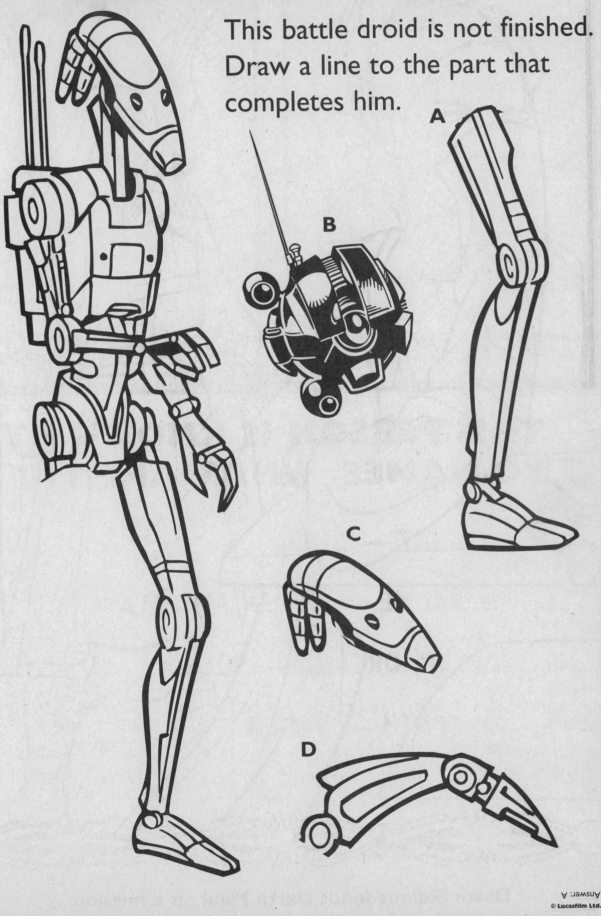

A

B

C

D

Darth Sidious sends Darth Maul on a mission...

...to capture the escaped Queen Amidala of Naboo. © Lucasfilm Ltd.

Darth Maul sends out probe droids to find the queen.

Qui-Gon Jinn will stop them.

Queen Amidala of Naboo

HELP THE QUEEN LAND
HER SPACE CRUISER ON THE PLANET BELOW.

START

FINISH

**Anakin runs from Darth Maul
while Qui-Gon Jinn prepares to protect him.**

Darth Maul pursues them on his Sith speeder.

Qui-Gon Jinn protects Anakin from attack.

**Darth Maul is a skilled fighter, trained
to use the dark side of the Force.**

**Qui-Gon and Obi-Wan wait to begin
negotiations with the Trade Federation.**

© Lucasfilm Ltd.

"I've got a bad feeling about this...."

Qui-Gon Jinn is a noble Jedi Master.

TRADE FEDERATION
WORD SCRAMBLE

Unscramble the words below to see Darth Sidious's command to Nute Gunray.

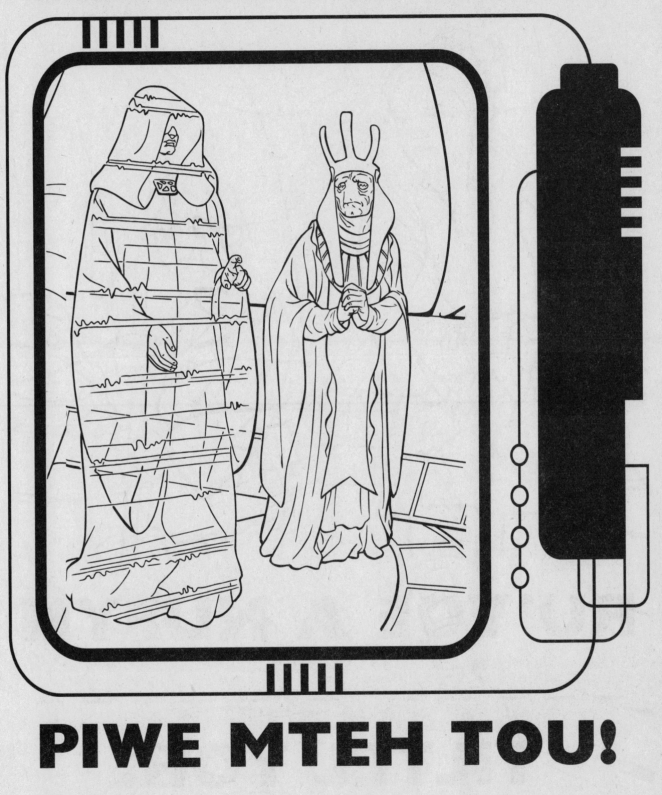

PIWE MTEH TOU!

– – – – – – – – – – – –

QUEEN AMIDALA'S WORD SCRAMBLE

Unscramble the words below and see the Queen's first words to young Anakin.

RU'YOE A NUFYN

,
_ _ _ _ _ _ _ _ _ _ _ _

TILTEL YOB.

_ _ _ _ _ _ _ _ _

Qui-Gon's apprentice is Obi-Wan Kenobi.

ESCAPE THE DESTROYER DROIDS

Help Qui-Gon and Obi-Wan get away from the Destroyer droid.

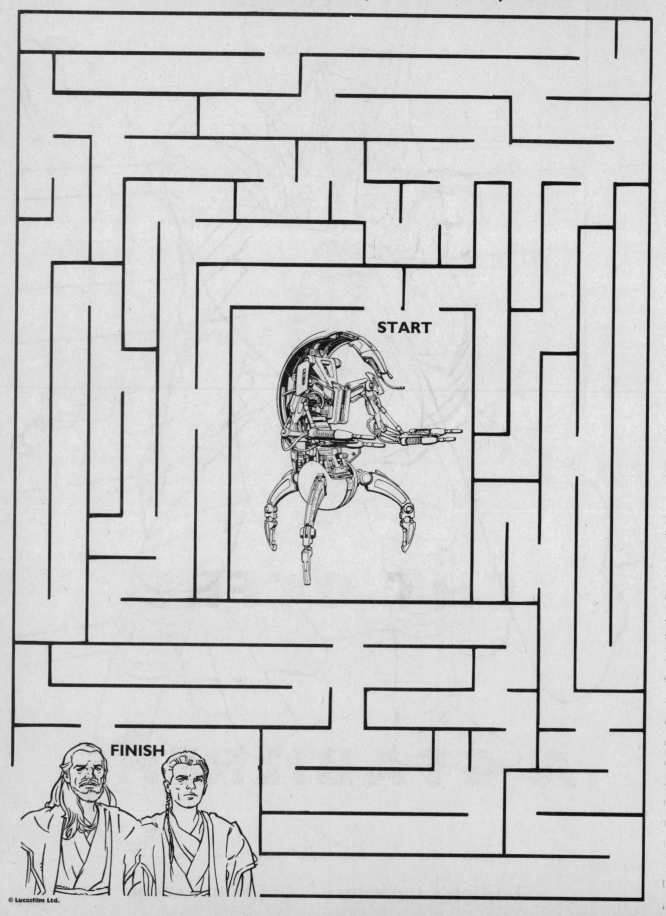

START

FINISH

JEDI WORD SCRAMBLE

Unscramble the words below to see what Obi-Wan's two greatest weapons are.

EHT OCFRE

_ _ _   _ _ _ _ _

A GTABILREHS

_ _   _ _ _ _ _ _ _ _ _ _

Padmé meets Anakin for the first time.

The Force is strong with Anakin Skywalker.

Qui-Gon Jinn defends himself...

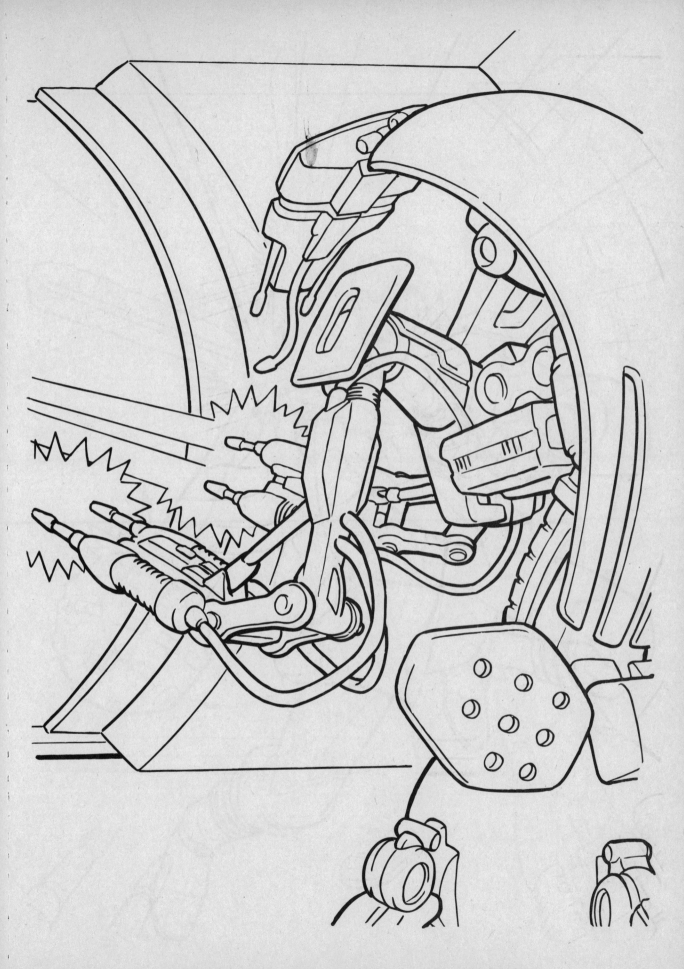

...against the fierce destroyer droids.

Obi-Wan Kenobi also defends himself...

...when attacked by the battle droids.

© Lucasfilm Ltd.

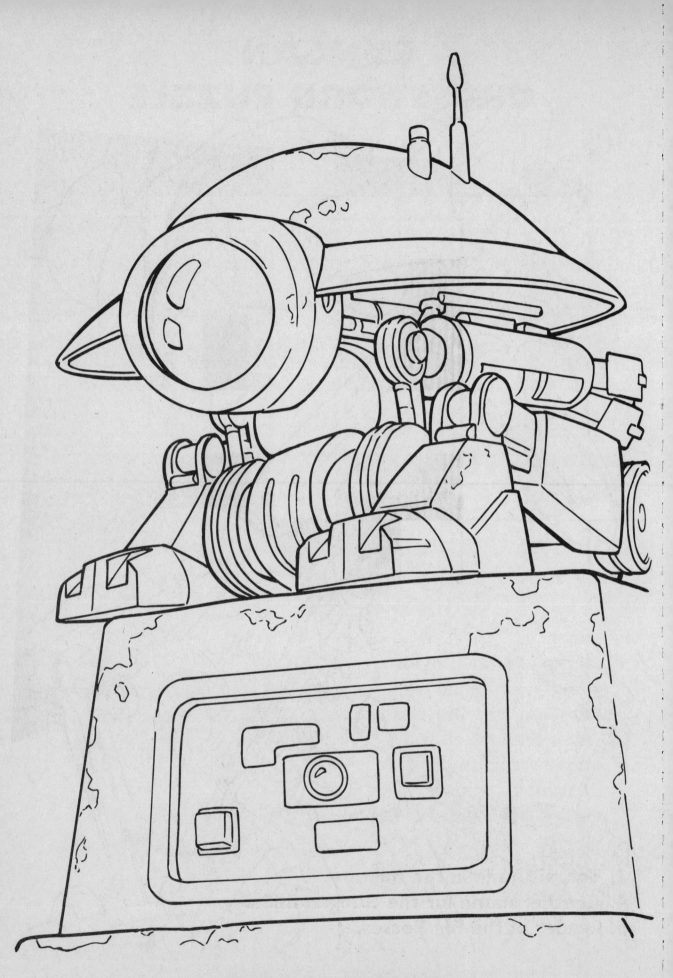

pit droid (deactivated)

GUNGAN CROSSWORD PUZZLE

Down:
1. Name of the Gungan who "greets" Jar Jar, Qui-Gon and Obi-Wan when they reach the underwater city.
2. Becomes a general before the battle of Naboo

Across:
3. Tarpals' rank in the military.
4. Another name for the Gungan military.
5. Leader of the Big Bosses.

WHO AM I?

I was a Padawan of Qui-Gon. I promised to train young Anakin as a Jedi.
I hid the offspring of Skywalker. I was struck down in a lightsaber duel.

A. YODA

B. DARTH SIDIOUS

C. LUKE SKYWALKER

D. OBI-WAN KENOBI

Your answer: _____

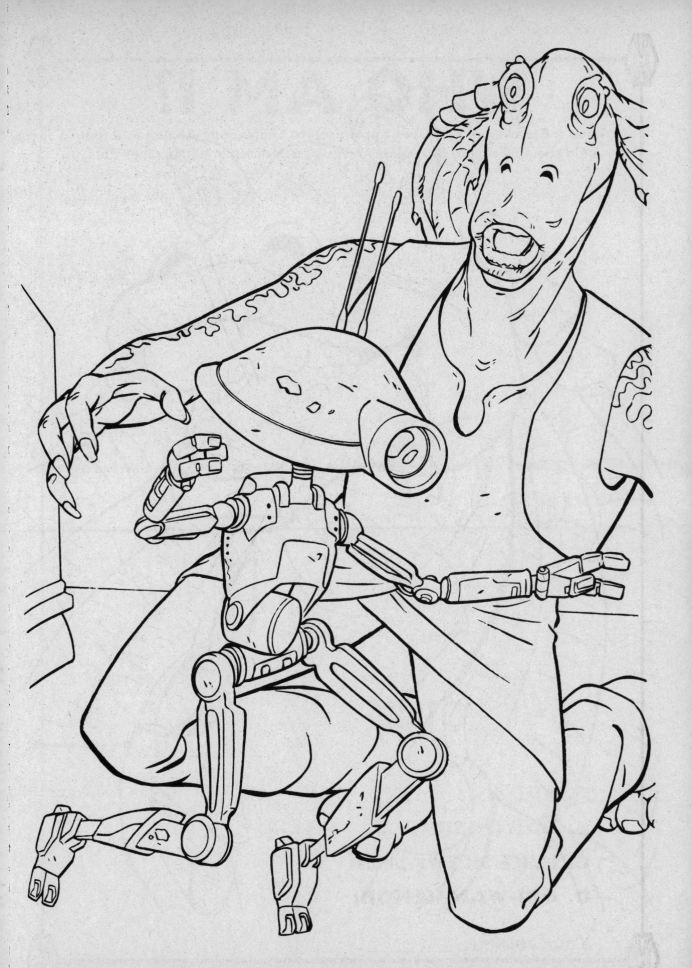

Jar Jar Binks is surprised when he activates a pit droid.

Jar Jar Binks

**Jar Jar is excited about making a new friend,
the poweful Jedi Qui-Gon Jinn.**

The Force flows through the Jedi.

**Qui-Gon and Obi-Wan meet
Boss Nass, chief of the Gungans.**

He is called "Big Boss Nass" for a good reason.

© Lucasfilm Ltd.

**A Gungan bongo provides the Jedi
with transport through the planet's core.**

There are many dangers going through the planet core, like this opee sea killer.

© Lucasfilm Ltd. **The opee sea killer attacks the Jedi in their bongo.**

Watch out for the sando aqua monster.

"There's always a bigger fish...."

Jar Jar is frightened.

Anakin in the marketplace in Mos Espa.

Anakin leaves his mother.

© Lucasfilm Ltd.

KAADU CORRAL

Which square completes the drawing?

A   B   C   D

Your answer: _____

WHAT IS THE NAME OF THEIR PEOPLE?

A. THE JEDI OF CORUSCANT

B. THE KAMINOANS OF KAMINO

C. THE JAWAS OF TATOOINE

D. THE GUNGANS OF NABOO

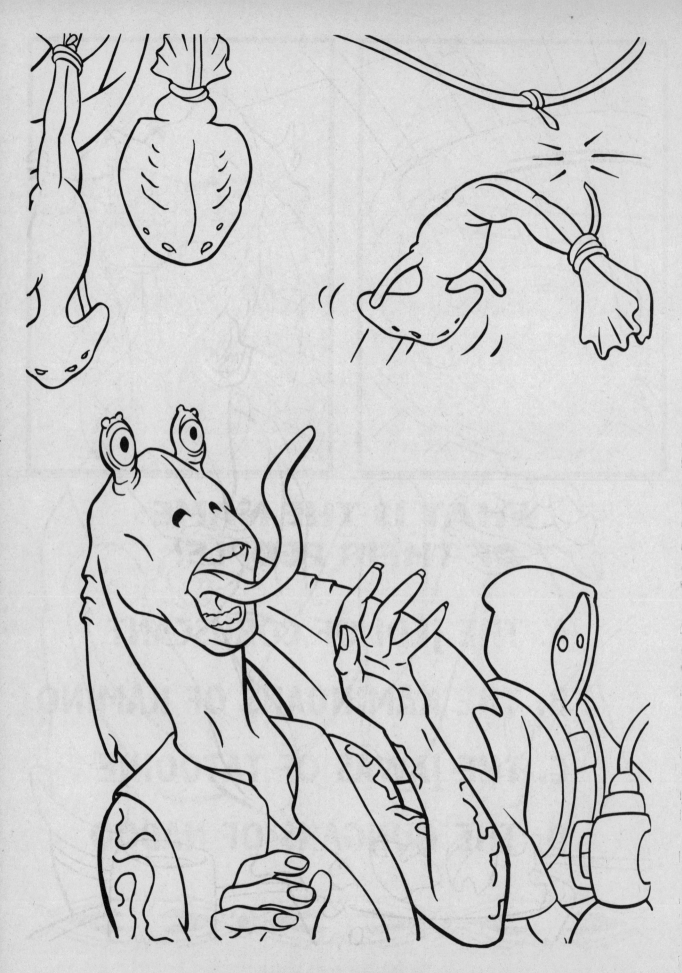

Jar Jar is clumsy...

...and that annoys Sebulba.

Gungans prepare for battle.

"Meesa be tinkin weesa got a grand army..."

**Viceroy Nute Gunray communicates
with a hologram of Darth Sidious.**

**Darth Sidious commands his apprentice,
Darth Maul, to do his evil bidding.**

Qui-Gon Jinn ignites his lightsaber...

...in a spectacular duel with Darth Maul.

The battle rages on...

THE JEDI ORDER

Which square completes the drawing?

A   **B**   **C**   **D**

Your answer: _____

DARK SIDE OF THE FORCE CROSSWORD PUZZLE

Down:
1. Last Sith apprentice to Emperor Palpatine.

Across:
2. _____ Skywalker, father of Luke.
3. The _____ are the sworn enemy of the Jedi.
4. Darth _____ is the Master of Darth Vader.
5. The color of Darth Vader's lightsaber.

Answers: 1. Darth Vader, 2. Anakin, 3. Sith, 4. Sidious, 5. red

**They cross lightsabers as they attack
each other, trying to gain the upper hand.**

© Lucasfilm Ltd.

Obi-Wan joins the battle.

Darth Maul's lightsaber has two blades.

© Lucasfilm Ltd.

Darth Sidious uses the dark side of the Force.

© Lucasfilm Ltd.

**Qui-Gon, Obi-Wan and Anakin all use
the good side of the Force.**

© Lucasfilm Ltd.

**Obi-Wan Kenobi promises to train Anakin
in the ways of the Force.**

Yoda sits in his chair in the Jedi Council.

Mace Windu is a strong Jedi Master.

WHERE DID ANAKIN LIVE
BEFORE HE MET QUI-GON?

A. NABOO

B. MOS EISLEY

C. MOS ESPA

D. SKYWALKER RANCH

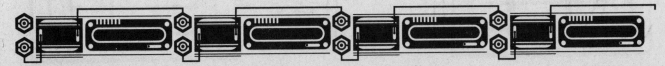

JABBA'S PALACE MAZE

Help Watto find his way through the maze to place his bet with Jabba the Hutt.

START

FINISH

The Jedi must deal with all sorts of characters to keep peace in the galaxy.

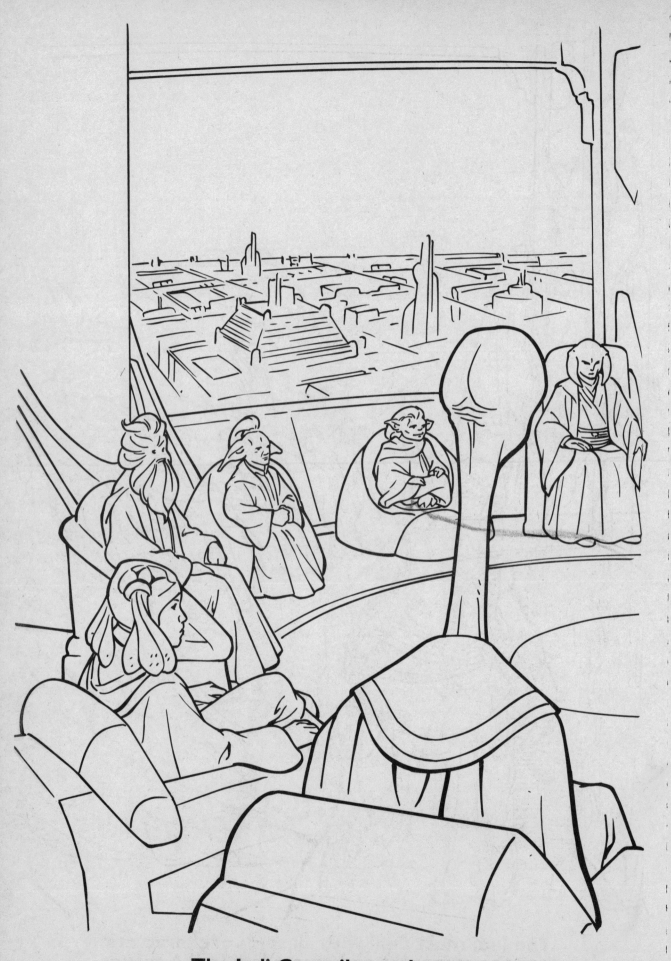

The Jedi Council members...

...are the strongest and wisest Jedi in the galaxy.

© Lucasfilm Ltd.

Anakin Skywalker answers questions from the Jedi Council.

Mace Windu is a leader in the Jedi Council.

**The imposing Saesee Tiin and the beautiful
Depa Billaba are members of the Jedi Council.**

**Eeth Koth and Adi Gallia
are also members of the Jedi Council.**

Yarael Poof, Jedi Council member

EMERGENCY COUNCIL

Help Jedi Master Yarael Poof through the maze and back to the Jedi temple for an emergency meeting of the Jedi Council.

START

FINISH

© Lucasfilm Ltd.

CLONE TROOPER WORD SEARCH

Look forward, backward, across, down and diagonally to find these words.

human	clone	troops
Kamino	Jango	Fett
Geonosis	blaster	rifle

358264 9831

F	S	A	T	R	I	F	L	E
O	N	I	M	A	K	P	O	D
B	L	A	S	T	E	R	Y	A
J	A	N	G	O	F	E	T	T
Z	I	F	E	B	N	Q	R	J
H	U	M	A	N	U	O	A	T
L	O	N	E	E	O	S	E	N
H	Z	A	I	P	O	L	S	G
C	S	K	S	N	R	B	C	D

Ki-Adi-Mundi, Jedi Council member

Anakin Skywalker is a skilled pilot.

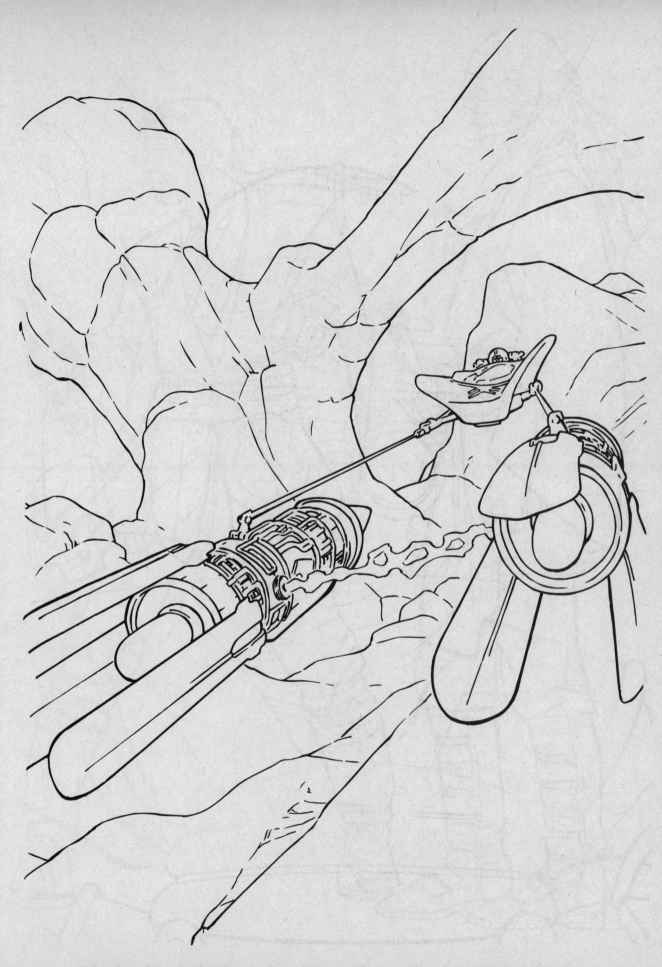

He is the only human who can control a Podracer.

A lightsaber is the weapon of the Jedi.

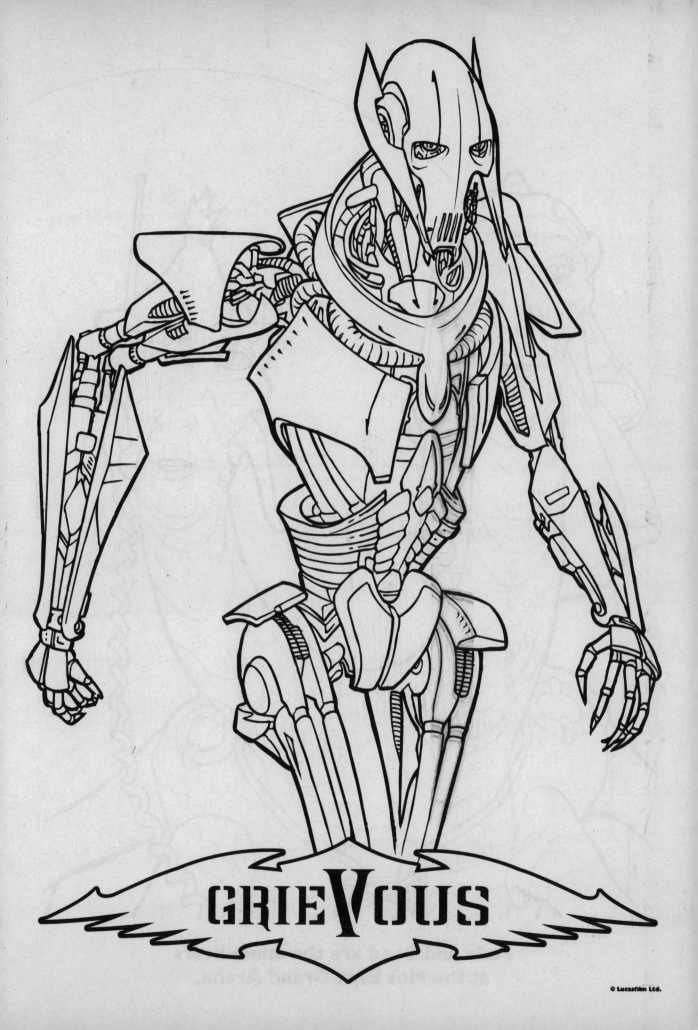

GRIEVOUS

Fode and Beed are the announcers at the Mos Espa Grand Arena.

Pit droids prepare for the big race.

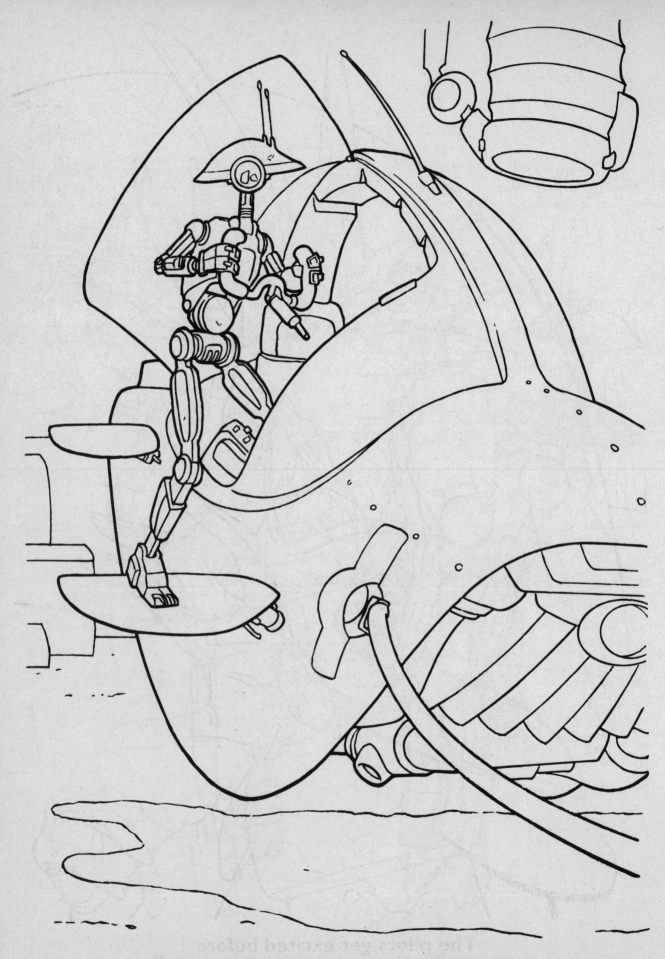

Pit droids help work on the Podracers.

**The pilots get excited before
the Boonta Eve Classic Podrace.**

Sebulba will do anything to win the Podrace.

"He always wins...."

This is Ben Quadinaros' first Podrace.

Hopefully his Podracer's energy coupling will hold together.

© Lucasfilm Ltd.

Each Podracer is different.

They are made to go very fast.

Big engines...

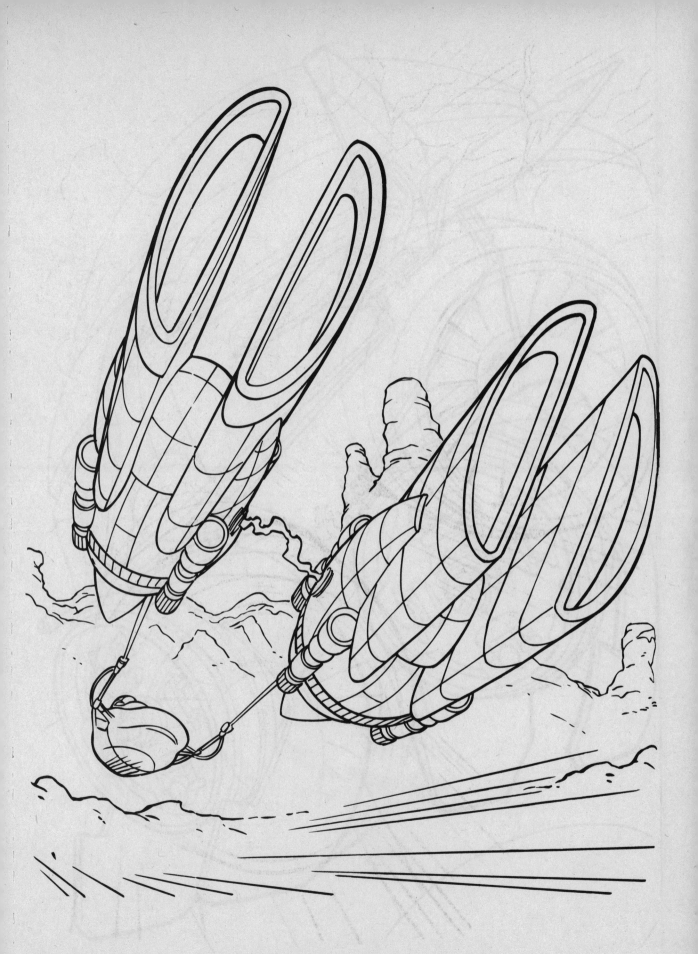

...pull the small Podracer along.

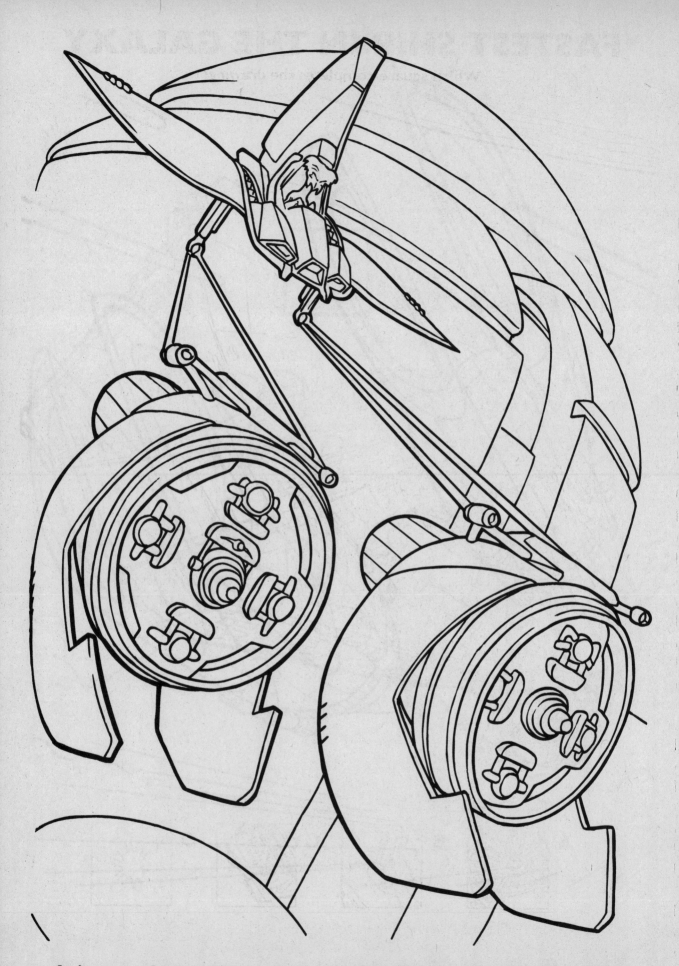

It is very dangerous to Podrace. It's illegal on most systems.

FASTEST SHIP IN THE GALAXY

Which square completes the drawing?

A   B   C   D

Your answer: _____

WHAT FLOWS THROUGH A JEDI AND GIVES HIM STRENGTH?

A. LIFE BLOOD

B. ANCIENT WISDOM

C. BLUE LIGHTNING

D. THE FORCE

Anakin has special abilities. The Force is strong with him.

Anakin is a skilled pilot.

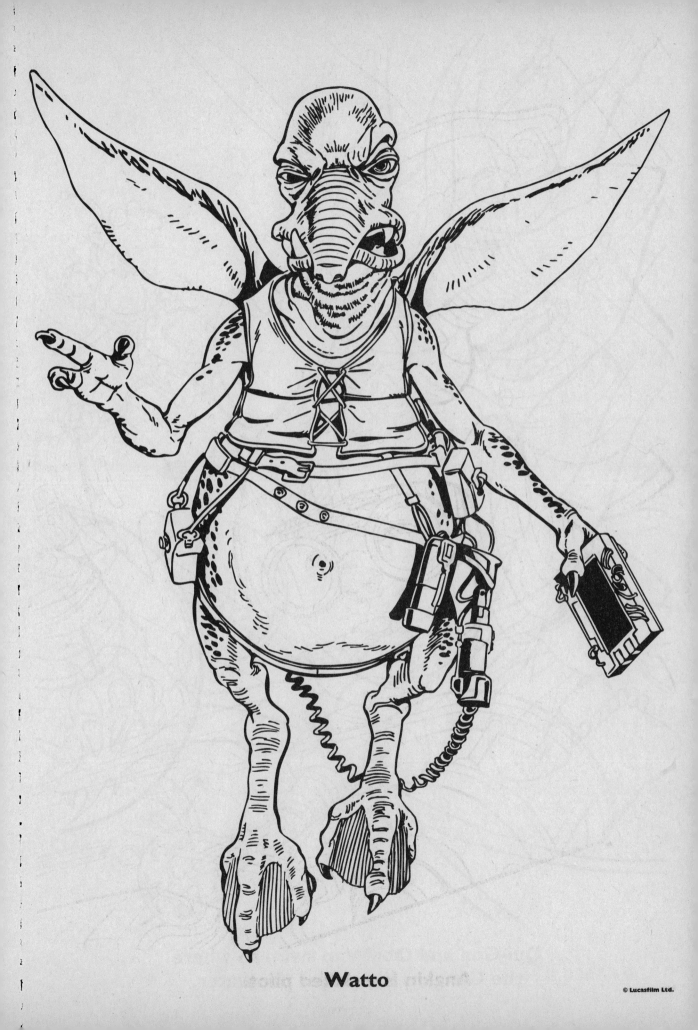

Watto

Qui-Gon and Obi-Wan swim to where the Gungans live under the water.

Jar Jar leads them there.

"Wipe them out... all of them."

There can be only two Sith, a Master and an apprentice.

© Lucasfilm Ltd.

Jedi have apprentices too.

DARTH MAUL'S SITH INFILTRATOR

Only a Sith could navigate through this maze.

START

FINISH

© Lucasfilm Ltd.

WHO AM I?

I am a Wookiee from Kashyyyk. I am a friend and co-pilot of Han Solo.

A. JABBA THE HUTT   B. WATTO

C. CHEWBACCA   D. BOBA FETT

Your answer: _____

Answer: C.

Jedi are guardians of the peace in the galaxy.

Captain Tarpals will defend his home...

...against the invasion of the battle droids.

Anakin will race fairly... and win!

Sebulba will cheat... and lose.

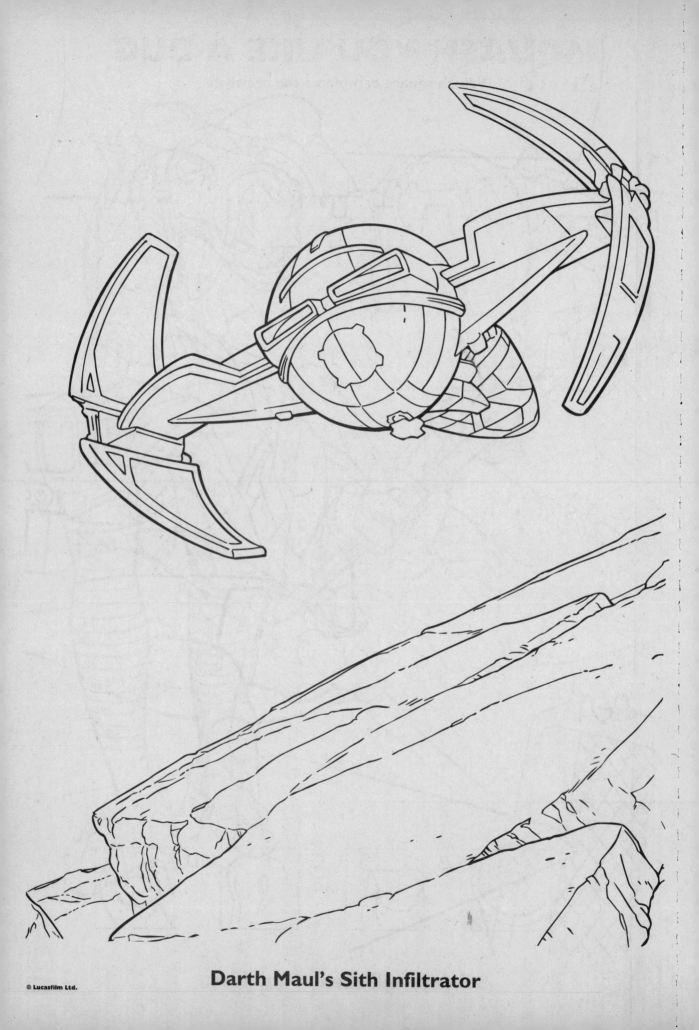

Darth Maul's Sith Infiltrator

SQUASH YOU LIKE A DUG

Which square completes the drawing?

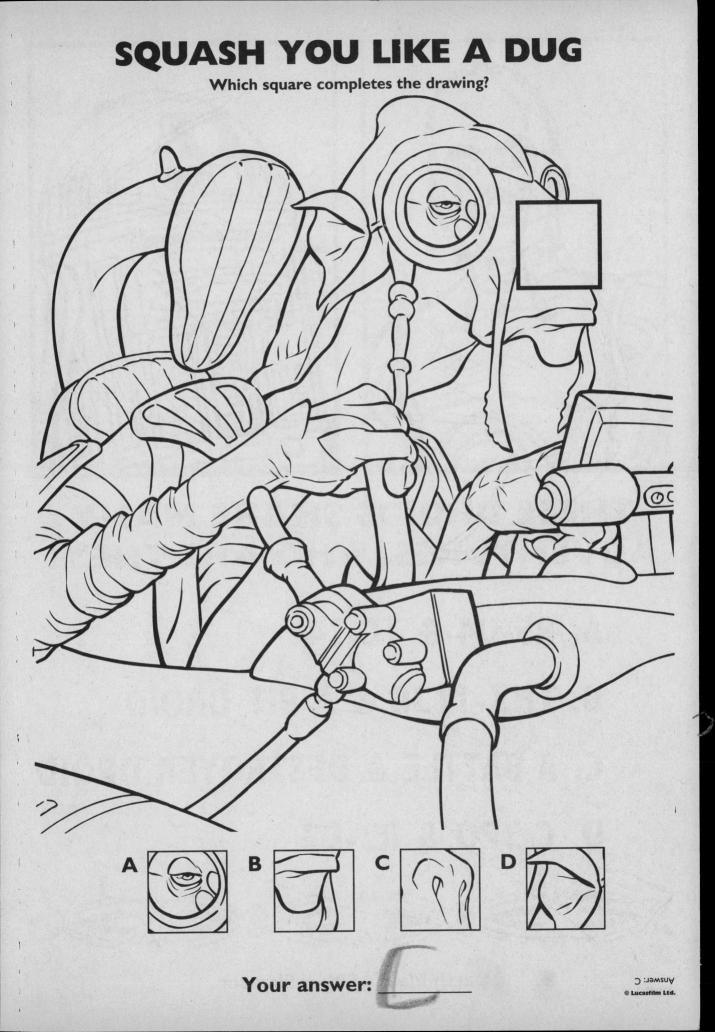

A **B** **C** **D**

Your answer: _____

THESE DROIDS SHARE MANY ADVENTURES. WHO ARE THEY?

A. R5-D4 & TC-14

B. THX-1138 & A PIT DROID

C. A BATTLE & DESTROYER DROID

D. C-3PO & R2-D2

A Trade Federation control ship

**"Inform the Viceroy that the ambassadors
wish to board immediately."**

**The ambassadors' ship arrives in the hangar
of the Trade Federation control ship.**

**The Gungans use heavy weapons
to defend their home against the invasion.**

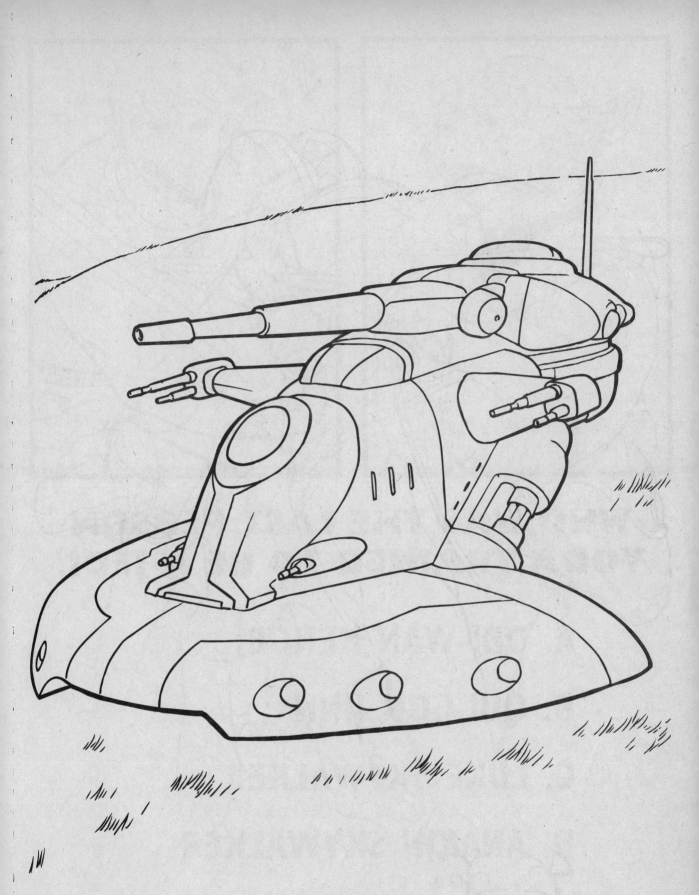

The battle droids have heavy weapons, too.

WHO WAS THE LAST PERSON YODA TRAINED TO BE A JEDI?

A. OBI-WAN KENOBI

B. QUI-GON JINN

C. LUKE SKYWALKER

D. ANAKIN SKYWALKER

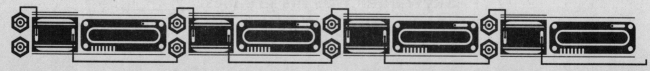

IMPERIAL CROSSWORD PUZZLE

Down:

1. Senator from Naboo, later became Supreme Chancellor.
2. After becoming Supreme Chancellor, he declared himself _____.

Across:

3. Darth _____ helped him hunt down and destroy the Jedi.
4. As a young Padawan learner, Anakin Skywalker was his greatest _____.
5. He saw the Jedi as a _____ to his power.

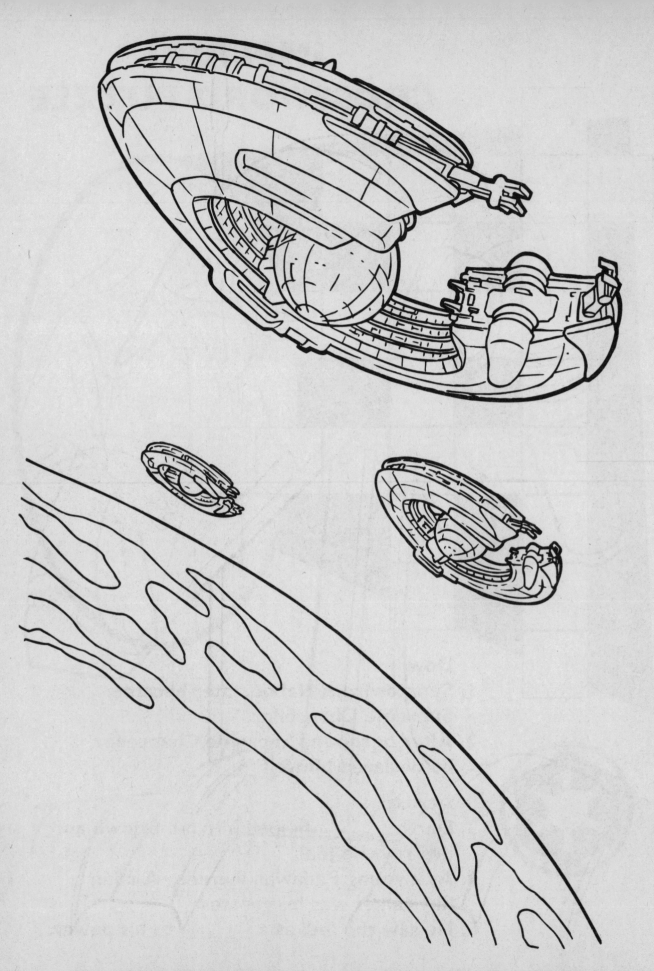

The Trade Federation controls the battle droid army.

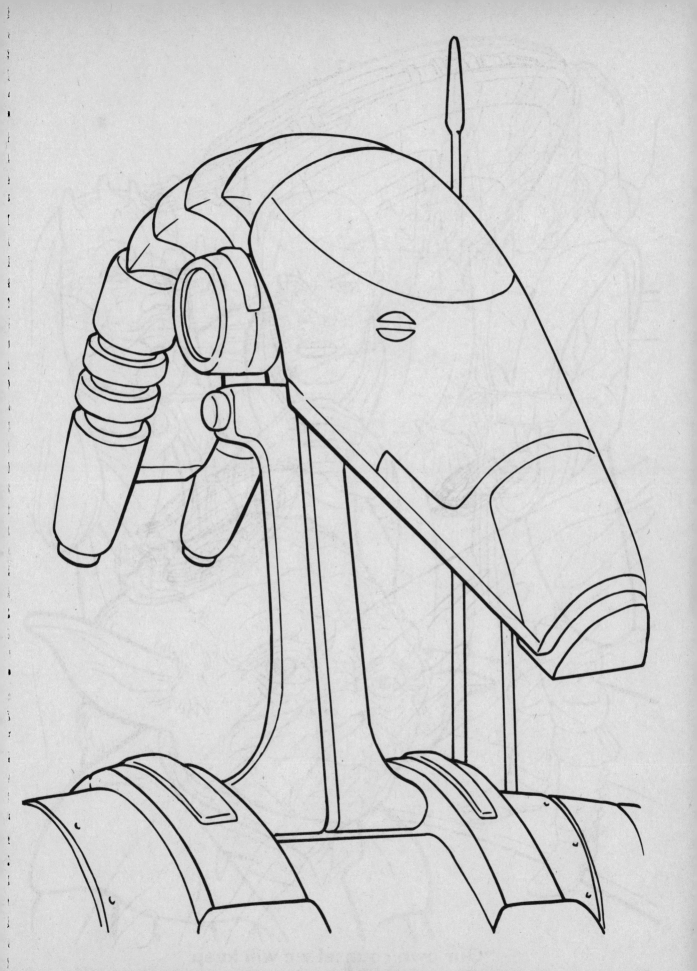

"Aye-aye, Commander... Roger... Roger..."

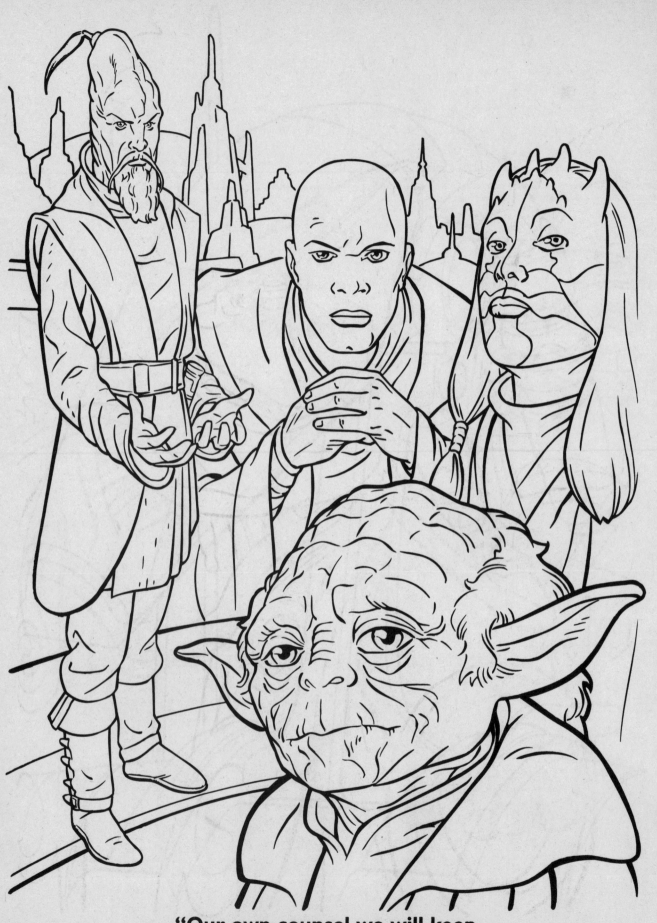

"Our own counsel we will keep
regarding who will be trained as a Jedi."

"Meesa thinks weesa being friends... Ha ha!"

REBEL ALLIANCE MAZE

Lead your squadron of X-wing fighters back to their secret Rebel base.

FINISH

START

The Queen makes a daring attempt to retake the palace.